ASIAPAC COMIC SI

GW01045901

Kaleidoscope of the
Wei-Jin Era

A NEW ACCOUNT
OF
WORLD TALES

Written by
Liu Yiqing

Edited and illustrated by
Tsai Chih Chung

Translated by
Alan Chong

ASIAPAC • SINGAPORE

Publisher
ASIAPAC BOOKS & EDUCATIONAL AIDS (S) PTE LTD
2 Leng Kee Road
#02-08 Thye Hong Centre
Singapore 0315
Tel: 4751777, 4751773
Fax: 4796366

First published July 1990
Reprinted June 1991

©ASIAPAC BOOKS, 1990
ISBN 9971-985-52-7

Cover Design by Eric Yong

Typeset by Avant Garde
Printed in Singapore by
Loi Printing Pte Ltd

Publisher's Notes

Comics play an important role in our fast-moving urban society. They serve the young as well as the adult readers. Comics are not only fun and entertaining, they can also be a kind of political satire and can even make classical literature and philosophy available to us in a light-hearted way.

A New Account of World Tales is yet another publication in the Asiapac Comic Series. The staccato dramas of the Wei-Jin Era are being captured on today's language through the popular cartoonist Tsai Chih Chung.

The 120 selected anecdotes in this book tell the stories of emperors, princes, high officials, generals, courtiers, urbane monks and lettered gentry of a turbulent time. They afford a stark and amoral insight into human behaviour in its full spectrum of virtues and frailties, and glimpses of brilliant Chinese witticisms too.

We feel honoured to have well-known cartoonist Tsai Chih Chung's permission to the translation right to his bestselling comics. We would also like to take this opportunity to thank the translator and typesetter for putting in their best efforts in the production of this series.

Other Titles in Asiapac Comic Series

The Book of Zen
The Sayings of Lao Zi
The Sayings of Zhuang Zi
The Sayings of Confucius
Wonderful World of Animals - Vol. 1
Roots of Wisdom

Introduction

A NEW ACCOUNT of WORLD TALES is an anthology of succinct anecdotes about people and human nature in its full spectrum of virtues and frailties. It is about emperors, princes, high officials, generals, courtiers, monks and the lettered gentry mainly of the Wei (AD 220 - 265) and Jin (AD 265 - 420) dynasties.

Though classified as a novel by some scholars because it contains some fictionalisation, the book is regarded by many as a valuable source of history for the era concerned. To begin with, the book was compiled around AD 430, just a decade after the close of the Jin dynasty — well within the lifetime of some of the protagonists. Most of the events and nearly all the 626 characters appearing in it have also been attested in other historical sources.

Traditionally, authorship of the book is credited to Liu Yiqing, a nephew of Liu Yu, the warlord who usurped the Jin throne and founded the Song dynasty (AD 420 - 479). Modern day scholars, however, generally believe it was compiled by Liu with the help of many of the scholars and staff who worked under his royal patronage.

Shi Shuo Xin Yu (A New Account of World Tales) — the name of the book used consistently since AD 710 — contains 1,130 concisely written stories, conversations, comments and short characterisations. Broadly, they fall under the headings of civic and moral virtues; cultivated tolerance and intellectual accomplishments; recluses and women; technology and art; and human frailties.

Many of the tales, written in classical Chinese, would not have been meaningful to modern readers without the excellent annotation by Liu Xiaobiao (AD 462 - 511) in the early sixth century. Liu's commentary was so well done that it has been hailed as one of the three greatest commentaries in Chinese literature.

Besides brevity of expression in the fashion of the Analects of Confucius and Dao Dejing of Lao Zi, *A New Account of World Tales* has another unique feature. The author merely attempts to tell a good story and that is it. It is left to the reader to draw any inference or lesson or pass any moral judgement on the event or the behaviour of the protagonists.

The Wei-Jin era was one of China's darkest ages. Civil wars, deadly factional intrigues and mass executions were the order of the day. After the Sima family wrested power from the ruling Cao family in a coup in AD 249, those who were or suspected to be loyal to the former Wei emperor were wantonly massacred. At a time when the utterance of a wrong word could result in the annihilation of three generations in a family, prudence was the secret for self-preservation.

The intelligentsia of the day, including those in public service, invented a seemingly foolproof method of avoiding personal disaster: *qing tan*, or literally, pure conversation. This called for conversations which avoided touching on politics and, indeed, anything to do with the real world. This way, no word could be misconstrued and held against the speaker. The abstract doctrines of Lao Zi and Zhuang Zi seemed to be ideal as subjects for discussion. One could talk for a long time without anyone knowing what one was actually talking about.

Soon, a new breed of self-proclaimed "ming shi" or famous gentlemen was born. They prided themselves on being remote and unconventional and talked in riddles. Some of these famous gentlemen indulged in drinking orgy, some pretended to be mad, yet others resorted to nudism and other bizarre behaviours.

As the vogue of pure conversation caught on, attitudes and values changed. Many members of the lettered gentry and high officials came to regard all mundane matters as vulgar. Administrators took pride in not handling the day-to-day affairs; local officials stopped being concerned about the people's welfare; and generals ceased bothering about military matters. The result was unprecedented corruption and decay of the society.

While the intelligentsia indulged in bizarre escapisms, the powerful and the rich took pleasure in debauchery and extreme extravagance. Emperor Wu of Jin kept more than 10,000 concubines and slept where his goat-carriage would stop. Every time Shi Chong, a wealthy man, held a feast, guests had to drain their cups or the maids who failed to persuade them in doing so would be killed.

These were signs of a sick society, a society where emperors and princes thought nothing of wiping out the entire families of siblings to gain power and inaction was a virtue.

A New Account of World Tales is a scrapbook of history for this turbulent era. It takes snapshots, as it were, of the kaleidoscope of contemporary personalities and events and presents them starkly and amorally. If only we, the readers, appreciated the inner woes of Liu Ling the drunkard, we would, perhaps, forgive him for being perpetually drunk.

This cartoon interpretation of the original work focuses on 120 anecdotes. Through the stories and words of more than a hundred characters, readers will gain a good insight into the mood and socio-political milieu of the Wei-Jin era.

A glossary of the protagonists appear at the back of the book.

Alan Chong

Alan Chong is a freelance writer and translator.

About the Editor/Illustrator

Tsai Chih Chung was born in 1948 in Chang Hwa County of Taiwan. He began drawing cartoon strips at the age of 17 and worked as Art Director for Kuang Chi Programme Service in 1971. He founded the Far East Animation Production Company and the Dragon Cartoon Production Company in 1976, where he produced two cartoon films entitled *Old Master Q* and *Shao Lin Temple*.

Tsai Chih Chung first got his four-box comics published in newspapers and magazines in 1983. His funny comic characters such as the Drunken Swordsman, Fat Dragon, One-eyed Marshal and Bold Supersleuth have been serialized in newspapers in Singapore, Malaysia, Taiwan, Hong Kong, Japan, Europe and the United States.

He was voted one of the Ten Outstanding Young People of Taiwan in 1985 and acclaimed by the media and the academic circle in Taiwan.

The comic book *The Sayings of Zhuang Zi* was published in 1986 and marked a milestone in Tsai's career. Within two years, *Zhuang Zi* went into more than 70 reprints in Taiwan and 15 in Hong Kong and has to-date sold over one million copies.

In 1987, Tsai Chih Chung published *The Sayings of Lao Zi*, *The Sayings of Confucius* and two books based on Zen. Since then, he has published more than 20 titles, out of which 10 are about ancient Chinese thinkers and the rest based on historical and literary classics. All these books topped the bestsellers' list at one time or another. They have been translated into other languages such as Japanese, Korean and Thai. Asiapac is the publisher for the English version of these comics.

Tsai Chih Chung can be said to be the pioneer in the art of visualizing Chinese literature and philosophy by way of comics.

Contents

A NEW ACCOUNT
OF
WORLD TALES

14

15

17

An Emotionless Face

1

Ji Kang, a grand-son-in-law of Cao Cao, was once an official of the Wei dynasty.

2

He lived harmoniously with others and was careful to avoid arguments. He was even more circumspect following a change of regime.

Wang Rong had befriended him for 20 years.

4

In the 20 years I've known Ji Kang, his face has never betrayed his emotion. His countenance has always remained the same.

The Fierce Horse Is Not For Sale

1. Yu Liang had a fierce and untameable horse.

2. This horse is too wild. We'd better sell it off.

3. That would mean transferring a scourge to another. How can we do that?

4. Of old, Sun Shuao won praise for killing a double-headed snake so that passers-by would not come to harm.

5. Isn't it right to follow his example?

Ruan Yu Burns His Carriage

1 While residing in the Shan county, Ruan Yu never refused anyone who asked for the use of his splendid carriage.

2 Once, a man wanted to borrow the carriage for his mother's funeral but didn't dare ask for it.

3 What's the use of having a carriage when someone in urgent need didn't dare ask for it?

When Ruan came to know about it, he burnt his carriage.

Chu Pou the Taciturn Man

22

Xie An Teaches His Son

Xie An's wife always taught her son personally.

I've never seen you teach your child.

I'm teaching him constantly.

Teaching with deeds is better than teaching with words. A father's conduct is the best example for children.

The Eyes and The Moon

At the age of nine, Xu Ruzi was playing in the courtyard on a full-moon night.

Let's see how smart you are. Would the moon be brighter if the dark shadows in it disappeared?

Not necessarily. Our eyes, for instance, wouldn't be able to see if the pupils were absent.

Stealing Wine

1

Kong Rong, a descendant of Confucius, had two children; one aged five and the other six.

2

While father was having a nap one day, the younger one helped himself with some wine.

3

Hey, you're stealing father's wine. Bow to say thank you!

4

Since it's stolen, who cares about rites!

Weeping like a Bunch of Chu Captives

1

Having fled south from the northerns' invasion, officials of the Jin dynasty often gathered at the suburb of Xin Ting to feast on the beautiful scenery.

2

It's beautiful here but it can never be the same as our northern homeland.

3

4

Premier Wang Dao stood up in anger and said:

We should unite and strive hard to regain our territory. What's the use of weeping like a bunch of Chu captives?

Advantage of a Language Barrier

1

Reverend Srimitra, a monk from Central Asia who visited the court of Eastern Jin, didn't speak the Chinese language.

2

He communicated solely through an interpreter.

3

When Zhou Yi, a high official, was murdered, he chanted in his wake a long prayer which nobody understood.

4

Why doesn't the Reverend learn our language?

Because not knowing our language saves him a lot of trouble of social entertainment.

5

Through The Eyes of A Dharma Master

1

Sima Yu, the future Emperor Jian Wen of Eastern Jin, admired the virtues of dharma master Zhu Fashen and invited him for a short stay in the palace. Liu Dan asked:

2 How come that you, a monk, are enjoying yourself in a luxury home?

3 To you, this is a luxury home; but to me, it's just like a mat shed.

Secret of Keeping a Beautiful Whisk

Yu Fachang, an emigrant monk living in the capital of Eastern Jin, had an extremely beautiful horse-tail whisk which he carried wherever he went.

1

How do you manage to keep such a beautiful whisk with you?

One day, he visited Yu Liang.

2

The non-avaricious wouldn't ask me for it, and the avaricious who asked never got it from me. So it remains in my hand.

3

The Monk Who Keeps Horses

1 Zhi Daolin, a native of Henei, was a cultivated and influential monk of Eastern Jin.

2 He loved horses and always kept a few of them.

3 A holy man doesn't look nice keeping horses.

4 Worldlings love the physical form of the horse but I value its divine swiftness.

People'll Miss My Laxity

1 As premier of Eastern Jin, Wang Dao was noted as a liberal and mild administrator.

2 In his final years, he was somewhat less attentive to state affairs.

3 Premier Wang is too lax indeed.

True.

4 People say I'm too lax, but those who come after me will miss my laxity.

Perfect Divination

1. Zheng Xuan went for further study under Ma Rong.

2. For three years, he never saw his teacher but was taught only by Ma's top disciple.

3. One day, Ma Rong was stumped by a calculation on the celestial sphere.

4. Perhaps Zheng Xuan can solve this problem.

   Oh?

5. A smart chap indeed! He's solved it so quickly.

6. Zheng bade Ma farewell upon completion of his term of study.

Plagiarism

Xiang Xiu was considered the best among dozens of commentators of the Wei and Jin Era on the classic "Zhuang Zi". But he died before completing two chapters.

1

Guo Xiang, learned but mean, managed to secure a copy of Xiang's uncirculated work.

2

He continued from where Xiang left off and altered the commentary on another chapter.

3

4

Excellent commentary.

Following the publication of Guo's exegesis on "Zhuang Zi", Xiang's work was also discovered.

5

Hey look, aren't they the same?

Hence the existence of two separate versions of the commentary on "Zhuang Zi" bearing names of the two authors but having similar contents.

A Discourse on the White Horse

1 When he was young, Xie An asked Ruan Yu to explain to him the famous Discourse on the White Horse. Gongsun Long, a Zhao State dialectician, argued that a white horse was not a horse ...

2 I know you explained very well.

3 But I still cannot follow the argument!

4 Gosh! Exponents of the White Horse Discourse are a rare bread nowadays. So are those able to understand it!

Explanation for Dreams

Why do people dream of the coffin when they're about to gain offices and dream of excrement when they're about to gain wealth?

Someone asked Yin Hao:

Offices are basically stinking decay; hence they dream of the coffin.

Wealth is like faeces and dirt; hence they dream of excrement.

Infatuation with Dao De Jing

1

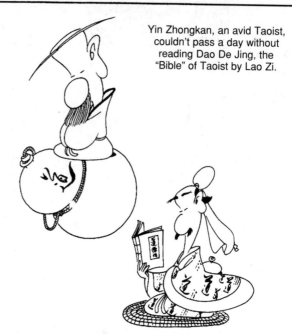

Yin Zhongkan, an avid Taoist, couldn't pass a day without reading Dao De Jing, the "Bible" of Taoist by Lao Zi.

He brought along the classic wherever he went.

The base of my tongue becomes stiff and my speech, bland, if for three days I don't read the "Dao De Jing".

2

3

A Poem in Seven Paces

1. Cao Zhi, talented and witty, won the heart of his father. Cao Cao, who wanted to make him heir-apparent in place of Cao Pi, his eldest son.

2. Cao Cao died without changing the order of succession. Cao Pi ascended the throne and bullied Cao Zhi in every imaginable way.

3. Walk seven steps and compose a poem. Off with your head if you fail!

4. Boiling beans to make a soup,
Straining beans to use for stock.
The stalks are burning under the pot.
The beans are weeping in the pot.
We've grown from the same roots.
Why such haste for one to cook the other?

Obituary for a Woman

1

Xie An asked Lu Tui, superintendent of records:

Why is it that your father-in-law Zhang Ping wrote an obituary for his mother but not for his father?

2

A man's virtues, reflected in his conduct of affairs, are known by people:

3

Whereas a woman's virtues are known only at home. How else can they be made public if not eulogised in an obituary?

43

Ghosts of Clothes

44

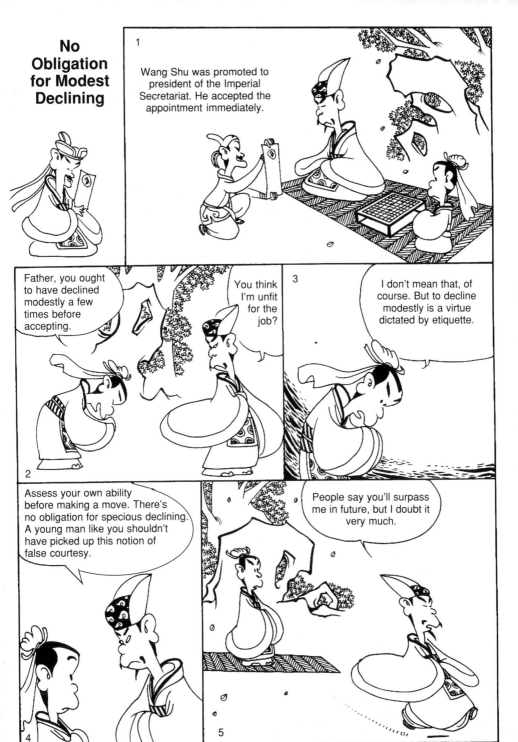

No Obligation for Modest Declining

1. Wang Shu was promoted to president of the Imperial Secretariat. He accepted the appointment immediately.

2. Father, you ought to have declined modestly a few times before accepting.

You think I'm unfit for the job?

3. I don't mean that, of course. But to decline modestly is a virtue dictated by etiquette.

4. Assess your own ability before making a move. There's no obligation for specious declining. A young man like you shouldn't have picked up this notion of false courtesy.

5. People say you'll surpass me in future, but I doubt it very much.

Playing the Zither Before Execution

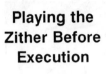

Ji Kang was talented but arrogant. He disdained all worldly things and refused to serve the emperor and the noble. Consequently, he offended the imperial court and was sentenced to death.

1

He showed no fear before his execution at Luoyang. As a last request, he asked to be allowed to play a tune.

Have you brought the zither?

2

The literatus and musician rendered his famous "Melody of Guang Ling" for the last time.

3

Yuan Xiaoni once asked to learn this melody but I refused to teach him. Now it is doomed for oblivion.

4

King Wen, who turned down a petition of clemency for Ji by 3,000 scholars, regretted later.

5

46

Son-in-law On the Eastern Couch

1
When grand tutor Xi Jian was at Jingkou, he despatched a disciple with a letter to premier Wang Dao, requesting a son-in-law from among his nephews.

Go to the eastern chamber and pick one for your master.

Yes, Sir.

2
On his return, the disciple reported to Xi:

The premier's boys are a fine lot, sir. All of them primmed themselves once they knew the purpose of my visit ...

3

Except one, lying on an eastern couch, showing not the slightest interest.

4
Pick that one!

5
The selected man was Wang Xizhi, who turned out to be one of China's greatest calligraphers.

The Midnight Call of Hu Jia

1 Liu Kun was besieged by the Hu cavalry and nobody could think of a plan to repulse the enemy.

2 In the night, Liu went up the city wall and sent deep, melancholic cries through the darkness.

3 The Hu soldiers were much affected by the sad ululation.

4 After midnight, Liu asked his men to blow the hu jia, a reed instrument native to the northerners.

5 Sounds of the hu jia made the Hu soldiers homesick. Before long, tears were rolling down their cheeks.

6 Unable to bear the homesickness evoked by the hu jia night after night, the Hu army retreated.

Liu Bei's Talents

1

You were formerly with Liu Bei in Jingzhou. What do you think of his ability?

Cao Cao asked Pei Qian:

2

Living in the Central Plains, he can stir the people to revolt but he can't conduct a stable government.

3

But ensconced in a rugged border area, he is able to take advantage of natural defences of the terrain and thrive as a regional hegemon.

A Timely Retreat

1. Zhang Han served under the Prince of Qi.

2. Rising autumn winds made him long for the wild rice and sliced perch delicacies of his home village.

3. How often can one be really happy in life? Why should I be taxing my brain wallowing in officialdom?

4. Thereupon, he resigned and returned to his home village.

5. Soon, the War of the Eight Princes broke out and the Prince of Qi was killed.

6. It was your foresight, and not the home village delicacies, that helped you to decide to make a timely retreat.

No, not at all!

Which is a happier choice: home village delicacies or a high position in the city? Just do what suits your fancy.

Wang Shu the Late Starter

1 Wang Shu was a late starter. In his younger days, people regarded him as an idiot. In deference to his father, however, premier Wang Dao employed him as his aide.

2 In frequent sessions of pure conversation, premier Wang was praised for whatever he said.

Right.

True.

Yes.

3 My master is not a saint. How can he be right in everything he says?

!

4 Premier Wang was much impressed by the remark, but his guests were chagrined.

You're right! Absolutely right!

5 What a tactless idiot!

He Has Not What Others Shouldn't Have

1 Huan Yi, who had a sharp eye for talents, was asked by Yu Liang to look out for a good officer for him.

Please get me an able man.

I'll try.

2 Huan Yi finally found Xu Ning after a year's search.

3 He's an unusual man. He may be lacking in some strong points which you find in others.

4 In that case, why do you still recommend him to me?

5 His unique quality is that he is devoid of all shortcomings which others shouldn't have.

The Twin Virtues of Yin Hao

Wang Xizhi on Personages

1

He exudes energy like a dragon in the wilderness.

Wang Xizhi on Xie Wan Shi:

2

On Zhi Daolin:
Pure at heart and elegant in manner.

3

On Zu Yue:
I don't think I'll meet another man so unique in manner and physical appearance like him.

4

On Liu Dan:
Like a towering tree with sparse branches and leaves.

56

He Knows Me Better Than I Do

Wang Meng and Liu Dan were equally renowned pure conversationalists.

1

They admired each other and had a profound friendship.

2

Wang Meng often said:

Liu Dan knows me better than I know myself.

3

A Lingering Friendship

1 Two good friends, Wang Gong and Wang Chen, became estranged as a result of alienation by a mutual friend.

2 Wang Gong could not forget his lovable friend. He missed him whenever there was a happy gathering.

3 On a stroll one morning, Wang Gong came to a budding parasol tree.

4 Dewdrops on the tender shoots were gleaming in the morning light.

Wang Chen is surely as clear and shining as these.

The Bull Is Better Than the Horse

1 On a visit to the Wu State, Pang Tong met many personages, including Lu Ji and Gu Shao.

2 Lu Ji is like a horse, capable of swiftness of foot; Gu Shao is like a bull, capable of carrying heavy loads over long distances.

3 Are you saying Lu Ji is superior to Gu Shao?

4 A horse maybe swift, but it can only carry one man at a time.

Though a bull can only travel 100 li * a day, it can carry many people.

*1 li = half km

The Three Zhuge Brothers

1

Zhuge Liang, his elder brother Jin and his cousin Dan, were all of high reputations. Each of them served in a different state of the Three Kingdoms.

2

There was a saying then that the state of Shu had got the dragon of the family, Wu, the tiger, and Wei, the dog.

3

In Wei, Zhuge Dan had a reputation for being fair in selecting candidates for offices.

4

In Wu, Zhuge Jin impressed with his magnanimity. Once, on a mission to Shu, where his brother Liang was a senior official, Jin restricted their contacts to public meetings and avoided private dealings.

A Man of Four Virtues

1 Contemporaries of Ruan Yu characterised him thus: In strength of character, he's inferior to Wang Xizhi;

2 In simplicity and elegance, he's not the equal of Liu Dan;

3 In graciousness and charm, he's no match for Wang Meng;

4 In intellectual power, he's below Yin Hao;

5 But he possesses the excellent qualities of them all.

He Is At Best Second Rate

1

Grand marshal Huan Wen came to visit Liu Dan in the capital.

2

I heard that the Prince of Kuanji has improved a great deal in his conversational skills. Is it true?

3

No matter how hard he strives, he can only be considered second rate.

4

Who can call themselves first rate?

5

You and I!

Strong In Expression but Weak In Argument

1 Liu Dan was having a pure conversation with Wang Meng in the presence of Wang's son.

2 Thanks for your hospitality. Goodbye.

Goodbye.

3 Father, how's Uncle Liu's conversational skills compared with yours?

4 In diction and preciseness of expression, he's inferior to me;

5 But in persuasiveness of argument and hitting the mark, I'm no match for him.

64

A Virtuous Man Talks Little

1 Calligrapher Wang Xizhi's three sons visited Xie An. Huizhi and Caozhi talked volubly about worldly matters.

2 But Xianzhi, the youngest, spoke merely out of courtesy.

3 Who's the best among the Wang brothers?

4 The youngest.

5 Why?

6 The words of a virtuous man are few; those of impetuous men, many.

The Debt of Suckling

1 Emperor Wu of Han was about to punish his wet nurse for an offence. She sought help from Dongfang Shuo, a courtier.

It's no use for me to plead with His Majesty.

2 When you leave after His Majesty has questioned you, look back at him several times and don't say a word. Maybe there's hope yet.

3 She did as she was told.

4 You old hag! Don't you expect His Majesty to remember the tenderness of the days you suckled him!

5 Ok, you're forgiven!

Thank you, Your Majesty!

Last Fling for the Emperor

1. Emperor Yuan of Jin was fond of drinking.

2. Even after the Jin dynasty had fled south from the northerners' invasions, he still indulge in it.
Premier Wang Dao often admonished him in tears.

3. Your Majesty should quit drinking and concentrate on the work of restoration.

4. Ok. Just one more cup.

Yes, Your Majesty.

6. After the last fling, the emperor turned the cup upside down and never drank again.

The Door's Too Wide

1
One day, when he was premier of Later Han, Cao Cao inspected the construction of the chancellery.

2
He wrote the word "huo", meaning alive, on the door-frame and departed.

活

3
Workers were baffled.

活

4
Yang Xiu, superintendent of records, saw it and said:

Dismantle the main entrance and make it smaller.

Why?

5
Adding "huo" to "men" (door), don't you have the word "kuo" meaning wide? The premier feels that the door is too wide.

That's right!

A Literary Gap of 30 Li

1. Cao Cao and Yang Xiu passed by a stone tablet dedicated to Cao E, the filial daughter of a man of the Han dynasty.

2. Hey, there are four pairs of characters on the reverse side.

黃絹　幼婦　外孫　鑿臼

3. Yang Xiu, do you know what they mean?

Yes, Sir.

4. Don't tell me. Let me think about them.

The Boy Who Stays in a Square

Panel 1

He Yan's mother was made a concubine of Cao Cao after his father's death.

Panel 2

This boy is really admirable. I'm thinking of adopting him as my own son.

Panel 3

Having known of Cao Cao's intention, He Yan drew a square on the ground and sat inside.

Panel 4

Why won't you budge from the square?

Because this is the house of the He family!

Panel 5

When Cao Cao came to know about it, he sent the boy away from the palace.

Ways of Keeping Warm in Winter

1

As a boy, Emperor Xiao of Jin wore only unlined clothes during the day in winter.

2

At night, he put on layers of cotton quilt.

3

Xie An admonished him:

Keeping too cold in the day and too hot in the night isn't the right way to keep Your Majesty healthy.

4

Daytime bustle keeps me warm; in the stillness of the night, I rely on layers of blanket.

The Generalissimo Disbands His Harem

Generalissimo Wang Dun, who enjoyed a great reputation as a lofty noble, once kept a seraglio of slave girls and concubines.

1

You're too indulgent in women to the detriment of your health.

2

Oh? I didn't realise it. But the solution is simple.

3

Thereupon, he disbanded his harem, allowing his women to leave freely.

4

The True Hero Beside the Couch

Cao Cao was to receive a Xiongnu envoy.

You stand in for me because my stature isn't impressive enough.

Yes, Sir.

1

2

Cui Yan, a man of imposing physique, received the envoy while Cao Cao stood beside the couch holding a sabre. After the audience, Cao sent a spy to ask the envoy:

3

How did you find the Prince of Wei?

The Prince of Wei was indeed impressive in appearance. But the man beside the couch holding a sabre was a true hero.

When Cao Cao learnt of the remark, he sent soldiers after the envoy and killed him.

4

5

Small in Stature, Big at Heart

Panel 1
Liu Ling was short,

Panel 2
And ugly looking.

Panel 3
Yet he was detached and carefree, roaming around and living an untrammelled life.

Panel 4
He always considered the universe too restricting.

The universe is really too small!

The Three Scourges of Yixing

In his younger days, Zhou Chu was a big bully in his native Yixing county.

At the same time, villagers there were terrorised by a vicious dragon in the river and a roving tiger in the forest. The three of them were called "the three scourges".

How do you compare with the dragon and the tiger?

Of course, I'm the strongest!

To prove himself, he went into the forest to kill the tiger

Self Renewal

1. In his younger days, Dai Yuan was a robber preying on merchants and travellers in the Jianghuai area.

2. On the way to Luoyang on leave, Lu Ji was spotted by Dai and his men.

Chief, here comes another quarry.

3. Hey, a man of your calibre shouldn't be wasting his time committing robberies!

4. Fine!

If only you'll help me, I'm prepared to start anew!

5. With the recommendation of Lu Ji, Dai started a career in government service at Luoyang. In the court of Eastern Jin, he rose to the rank of General Chastising the West.

Preface to the Lanting Collection

Wang Xizhi, Xie An, Sun Chuo and a group of literati gathered at Lanting in the Shanyin county to perform the rite of spring purification and compose poems. Wang was asked to write a preface for the resulting poetry collection.

1

Excellent!

2

3

This Preface to the Lanting Collection is comparable to the Preface to the Golden Valley Collection by Shi Chong.

Really?

Ha! Ha!

4

Wang would look extremely pleased whenever someone held him on par with Shi Chong.

Funeral Brays

1 Wang Can liked to listen to the braying of donkeys.

Bray

2 When he died, Emperor Wen of Wei came to offer his condolences.

3 Wang Can was fond of donkeys' brays; why don't you all make a bray to send him on his way?

4 Bray Bray Bray Bray

A Bray of Deference

Bray

1 Sun Zijing, a talented man, deferred to nobody except Wang Wuzi.

2 When Wang died, every personage of the day came to offer condolence. Sun came and cried uncontrollably at the wake.

3 You used to enjoy my imitation of the donkey's bray, so I'll do it once more for you.

4 Bray

5 Hee hee! Ha ha! Ha ha!

6 Damn it! Heaven allows you people to live and makes this man die!

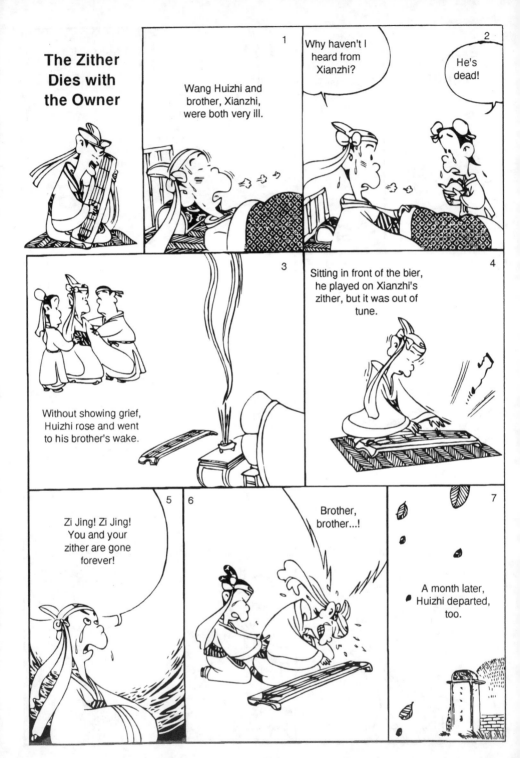

The Zither Dies with the Owner

1. Wang Huizhi and brother, Xianzhi, were both very ill.

Why haven't I heard from Xianzhi?

2. He's dead!

3. Without showing grief, Huizhi rose and went to his brother's wake.

4. Sitting in front of the bier, he played on Xianzhi's zither, but it was out of tune.

5. Zi Jing! Zi Jing! You and your zither are gone forever!

6. Brother, brother...!

7. A month later, Huizhi departed, too.

Fan Xuan Shuns Officialdom

Fan Xuan, a recluse living in the Yuzhang county, held aloof from the world.

1

All his life, he never entered the gate of any public office. Once, Han Kangbo, head of the county, was riding with him and trying to mislead him into visiting his official quarters.

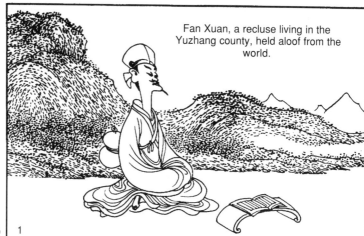

2

Fan jumped off from the rear of the carriage when he realised his friend's intention.

3

A Body Built for the Wilderness

1. Xu Yuan was fond of wandering among mountains and streams.

2. Hale and hearty, he climbed mountains with great agility.

3. Not only does Xu Yuan have a love for the wilderness,

4. He also has a body built for it.

Wang Zhan Chooses His Wife

Wang Zhan appeared a liitle idiotic while he was young. His father was worried that he might have difficulty getting a wife.

Pick a wife of your fancy.

1

I'd like to marry Hao Pu's daughter next door.

That's fine!

2

The bride turned out to be pretty and virtuous.

3

How did you know she's virtuous?

4

Once I saw her drawing water from the well. She kept her normal manner and never once did she cast an improper glance. That's how I judged her.

5

A Scapegoat

Premier Wang Dao asked Guo Pu to make a divination.

Bad news! Your Excellency is in imminent danger of being struck by lightning!

Any remedy?

Use a cypress tree.

A cypress tree trunk the same length of the premier was put on his couch.

Generalissimo Wang Dun, cousin of the premier, said:

You've escaped, but the cypress tree has suffered an undeserved disaster.

Perceptions of Weiqi

1

Weiqi, the game of encirclement chess which is also known as Go, meant different things to different people. Wang Tanzhi said:

Weiqi is a kind of sedentary retirement.

2

Zhi Daolin said:

Weiqi is a form of manual conversation.

Dotting the Eyes

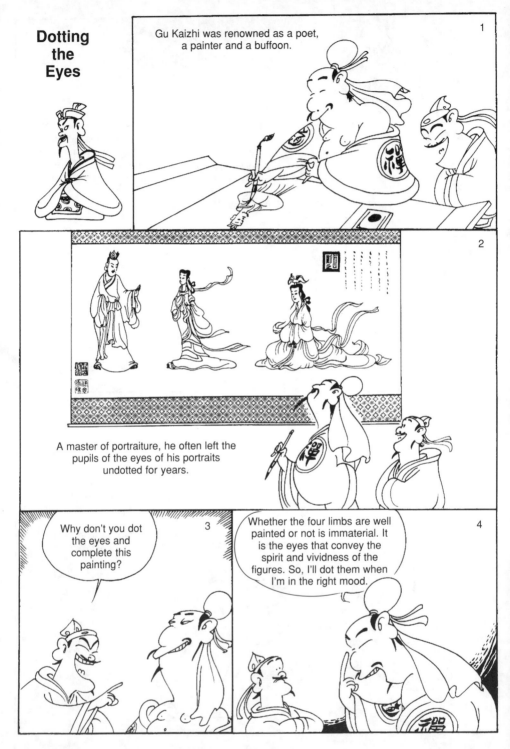

1

Gu Kaizhi was renowned as a poet, a painter and a buffoon.

2

A master of portraiture, he often left the pupils of the eyes of his portraits undotted for years.

3

Why don't you dot the eyes and complete this painting?

4

Whether the four limbs are well painted or not is immaterial. It is the eyes that convey the spirit and vividness of the figures. So, I'll dot them when I'm in the right mood.

Art of Painting

Master painter Gu Kaizhi said:

It's easy to paint "The hand sweeping over the five-stringed lute".

But it's very hard to paint "The eyes escorting the horning geese".

99

The Lure of Good Company

Ji Xun, a recluse-poet, stopped at the capital for a month.

Liu Dan found his conversations with him so absorbing that he visited him daily without fail.

If you stayed on much longer, I'd become a worthless capital intendant.

Seven Worthies of the Bamboo Grove

1

Ruan Ji, Shan Tao and Ji Kang were about the same age. Ji Kang was the youngest.

2

Liu Ling, Ruan Xian, Xiang Xiu and Wang Rong often joined them for merry revelry beneath a bamboo grove.

3

For this reason, people called them Seven Worthies of the Bamboo Grove.

An Empty Name After Death

1

Zhang Han did as he pleased without restraint. People called him "Foot soldier of Jiangdong".

2

You only live for present enjoyment; don't you care about leaving a good name for posterity?

3

An empty name after death is no better than a cup of wine at present!

The Ultimate Joy of Life

1 Bi Zhuo, President of the Board of Civil Office, was fond of drinking. One day, he was caught stealing from the official wine store.

2 What nonsense! You're fired!

Sorry, Sir.

3 He carried on drinking after being sacked.

4 What more to ask for in life than holding a crab claw in one hand and a cup of wine in the other and bobbing in a pool of wine?

One Turn in Ten Thousand Li

1. Zhou Yi and Wang Dao went to Ji Zhan's residence for revelry.

2. Tipsy, Zhou Yi misbehaved unashamedly.

3. How could you do this? You've always been prim and proper.

4. Like the Yangtze River, how can I avoid making at least one turn in ten thousand li?

108

Can't Pass a Day Without Bamboo

1. Wang Huizhi borrowed a vacant house for a short stay.

2. Plant a row of bamboo there.

3. Why all the trouble as it's only a short stay?

4. How can I pass a day without this pal?

An Impulsive Pleasure

1. Drinking and composing poems one snowy night at Shanyin, Wang Huizhi suddenly thought of his friend Dai Kui.

2. Boatman, please take me to Shan county.

3. After a night's voyage, he arrived at Dai's home but turned back without going in.

4. Let's go back.

5. Someone asked him:

Why didn't you see Dai Kui?

I went with an impulsive pleasure. When it dissipated, I returned. Why was it necessary to see Dai?

A Silent Encounter

1. Wang Huizhi was on a boat about to leave the capital when Huan Yi passed by in a carriage. Wang had heard that Huan, whom he had never met before, was good at playing the flute.

2. That's Huan Yi in the carriage.

Request him to play a tune.

4. Huan was then a very high-ranking official.

5. In deference to Wang's reputation, however, he agreed to the request and played three tunes.

6. As soon as it was over, the two parted with neither saying a word.

Soothing Wine

1

How does Ruan Ji compare with Sima Xiangru?

Wang Gong asked Wang Chen:

2

They're more or less equal in all aspects except the drinking habit.

3

Ruan Ji feels a sense of injustice, so he irrigates it with wine.

114

Forbidden Contribution

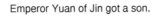

1 Emperor Yuan of Jin got a son.

2 A grand feast was held in celebration.

3 All ministers were presented with gift. Expressing his thanks, Yin Hongqiao said:

4 The birth of an imperial son is cause for universal rejoicing. Thy servant had no contribution in this matter, yet presented with such a sumptuous gift.

5 How could you have made any contribution in such a matter?

High Mountains and Deep Pools

1

Kang Sengyuan had deep-set eyes and a high nose. Premier Wang Dao often teased him:

Your eyes and nose are indeed weird looking!

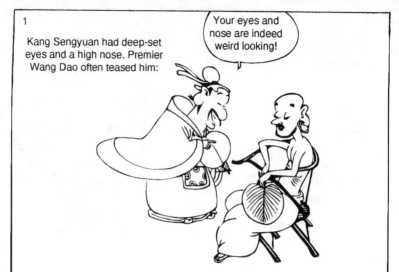

2

The nose is the face's mountain. If a mountain's not high, it's not dignified.

The eyes are the face's pools. If the pools are not deep, they're not clear.

3

A Gap for the Dog

1

Zhang Xuanzhi had a gap in his front teeth when he was eight.

2

Nobody dared to laugh at his dental condition because he was known for his caustic remarks.

3

Someone eventually teased him:

Why have you opened that dog hole in your mouth?

4

It's for people like you to get in and out.

Sunning Books in the Belly

1

On the seventh day of the seventh month, every household sunned its belongings.

2

3

Hao Long lay in the garden and bared his belly to the sun.

4

What are you doing here?

5

I'm sunning the books in my belly!

Chewing Sugarcane from the Top End

1. Gu Kaizhi was renowned not only as a painter but also for his idiosyncrasies.

2. When he chewed sugarcane, he always started from the relatively unsweet top end.

3. Why do you do that?

4. This way, it gets sweeter and sweeter, and more and more delightful.

Thirst Quenching Sour Plum

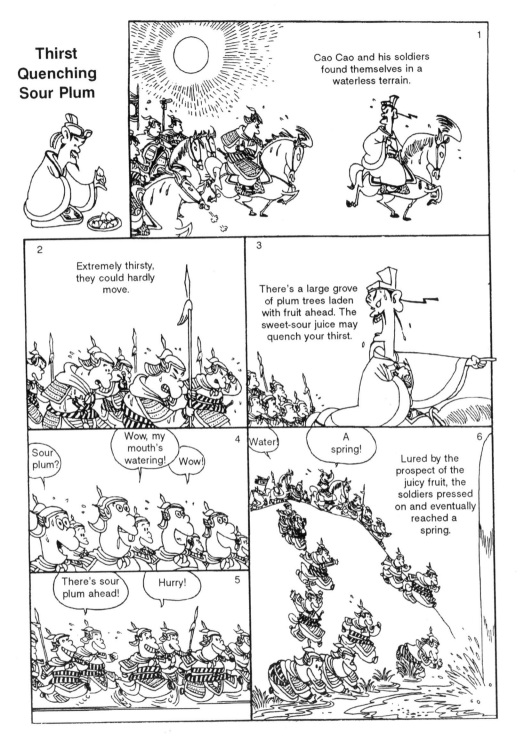

A
Drama
for
Real

122

The attendant died without knowing why. Others became convinced that Cao Cao really had the power of premonition. Schemers against him were deterred.

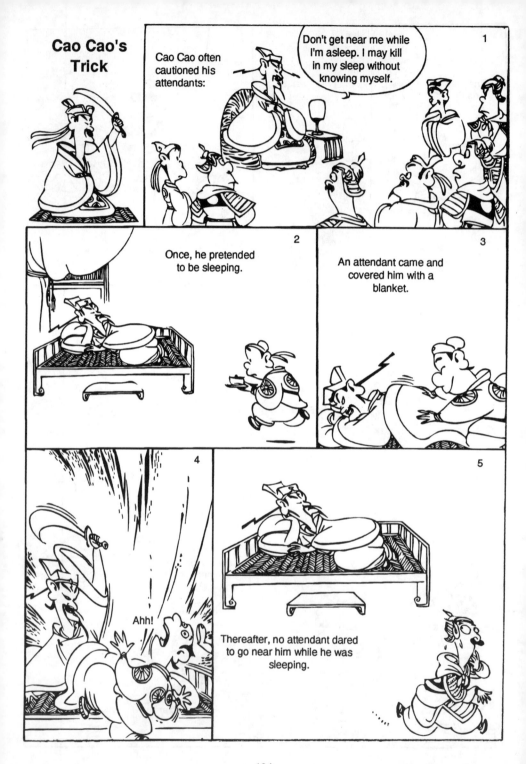

Ripping Sorrow

Huan Wen led an army into Sichuan. While passing through the Three Gorges, one of the soldiers caught a little monkey.

Its mother, clinging to the bank and crying pitifully, chased along for more than a hundred li and wouldn't go away.

2

Eventually, it plunged on board and died.

3

When its abdomen was cut open, all its entrails were found to have torn into pieces.

4

Get lost! I don't want a soldier like you!

Huan Wen was furious when told about it.

5

What Absurdity!

1. Yin Hao lived as a commoner recluse in the Xinan county after he was stripped of all official titles because of his failure in the northern campaigns.

2. All day long, he kept writing characters in the air.

3. Later, it was deciphered by people who followed his strokes that he was repeating in the four characters "duo duo guai shi" or "tut, tut, what absurdity!"

The Miserly Wang Rong

1 Wang Rong was extremely wealthy but very miserly.

2 His greatest interest was counting his wealth with his wife.

3 When his nephew got married, he sent only an unlined gown as a wedding present.

4 Soon after, he asked for the return of the gown.

Wang Rong Selling Plums

Wang Rong had some excellent plums which he sold regularly.

1

Wait a minute. These plums must be treated first before leaving this place.

2

For fear that others might obtain seeds of the plums, he bored holes through their kernels.

3

A Mercenary Father

1

Wang Rong lent a sizeable amount of cash to his daughter when she married Fei Wei.

2

Each time she came home for a visit, her father looked unhappy until one day ...

3

Dad, I'm repaying what I borrowed from you.

4

The debt cleared, smiles returned to Wang's face.

Hee! Hee! How are you keeping?

131

Fatal Lesson for a Songstress

Cao Cao owned a female entertainer with a golden voice but a vicious temper.

1

2

Sorry! I don't feel like singing today!

Damn it!

3

Thereupon, Cao Cao picked a hundred girls and had them trained in singing.

She's been picked from among the hundred girls and she sings just as well as you do.

Ah!

You can retire for good! Kill her!

Have mercy!

4

5

The Most Important Book of the World

1

Yuan Yue was eloquent and capable of disquisitions on "Intrigues of the Warring States", a book he often carried around.

2

In my youth, I studied "The Analects", "Lao Zi"...

He used to boast:

3

"Zhuang Zi" and "The Book of Changes". But all of them are useless.

4

Intrigues of the Warring States.

The most important book of the world is this.

5

He urged the Prince of Kuaiji, who held him in great esteem, to take sole possession of power at court. When Wang Gong got wind of it, he reported to Emperor Xiao Wu and had Yuan executed.

A
Shameful
Ignorance

Emperor Jian Wen saw rice in the padi field for the first time.

What grass is that in the field?

That's rice, Your Majesty.

Back in the palace, the emperor pondered over his ignorance for three days.

It's really a shame eating rice but not recognising the rice plant.

Moving Ants Sound Like Fighting Oxen

1

Yin Zhong Kan's father was afflicted with a strange illness which made him weak and extremely sensitive to sound.

2

Even the sound of ants moving beneath his bed was unbearable to him.

Are there oxen fighting under the bed?

No, just some ants crawling about.

3

Not knowing that the man was Yin Zhong Kan's father, Emperor Xiao Wu said:

I heard that an old man Yin has this strange illness ...

4

Oh! That's your father...

Thy servant is in a dilemma, not knowing what to do ...

137

Family Vendetta

1. Huan Xuan despised Huan Xiu, his cousin brother, and often humiliated him publicly.

2. An opportunity for revenge came when Xiu got wind that Xuan was about to usurp the throne.

Mother, I want to ambush Huan Xuan when he comes to visit you afterwards.

4. Huan Xuan's been brought up by me, too. He regards me as his own mother. I can't bear to see my own children kill each other ...

5. All right, forget about revenge.

Glossary

Bian Ju 卞鞠
　　An Eastern Jin dynasty official. Executed along with Huan Xuan who usurped the throne briefly in 404.

Bi Zhuo 毕卓 (Died AD 329)
　　An Eastern Jin dynasty official. In his youth, he was one of the "Eight Free Spirits", a group which registered its protest against the confinement of contemporary ritual conventions by resorting to all-night drunken orgies and unrestrained behaviour.

Cao Cao 曹操 (AD 155 – 220)
　　Founder of the Wei Kingdom. Though ostensibly the chancellor of the Eastern Han dynasty, he was its de facto ruler after AD 196. After his death in AD 220, his son Cao Pi deposed the last puppet Han emperor and proclaimed himself first ruler of the Wei Kingdom. Apart from his military prowess, Cao Cao was also an accomplished poet.

Cao Pi 曹丕 (AD 187 – 226)
　　Eldest son of Cao Cao and the first emperor of the Wei Kingdom. Like his father and younger brother Cao Zhi, he was also a prominent literary figure of his time.

Cao Zhi 曹植 (AD 192 – 232)
　　Third son of Cao Cao, he was gifted and well loved by his father. He is best known for composing a poem in the pace of walking seven steps under threat by Cao Pi.

Chen Taiqiu 陈太丘 (AD 104 – 187)
　　Though his highest post was only a magistrate of the Han dynasty, he enjoyed such a great reputation that 30,000 people attended his funeral.

Chen Zhongju 陈仲举 (AD 95 – 168)
　　An official of the Eastern Han dynasty well-known for his loyalty and uprightness. He was killed in AD 168 following a failed scheme to purge the government of eunuch control.

Chu Pou 褚裒 (AD 303 – 349)
　　A Eastern Jin dynasty general noted for his taciturnity.

Cui Yan 崔琰 (AD 154 – 216)
　　A man of impressive physical appearance who served as a provincial lieutenant-governor under Cao Cao. Suspected of treachery, he was eventually forced to commit suicide.

Deng Ai 邓艾 (AD 197 – 264)
A man of humble origin and a speech defect who rose to the rank of military governor-general during the Western Jin dynasty. Implicated in an attempted rebellion, he was executed with all his sons.

Dongfang Shuo 东方朔 (100 – 73 BC)
A quick-witted courtier who enjoyed great favour of Emperor Wu of the Han dynasty. Most of the stories associated with him appear to be legendary.

Dai Yuan 戴渊 (AD 260 – 322)
A pirate in his younger days, he was persuaded by one of his victims to start a career with the government. He rose to the rank of military governor-general in the Eastern Jin dynasty but was executed after failing in a factional struggle against Wang Dun.

Emperors of the Jin dynasty in chronological order

Emperor Wu 晋武帝 (AD 236 – 290)
Sima Yan (司马炎), founder and ruler of the Jin dynasty from AD 265 to 290. United China in AD 280. Thereafter, he led a life of decadence and extreme extravagance, with more than ten thousand concubines. Thus began the decline of the Western Jin dynasty and a prolonged period of factional rivalry and chaos.

Emperor Hui 晋惠帝 (AD 259 – 306)
Sima Zhong (司马衷), son of Emperor Wu. An idiot, he was largely a puppet during his reign from AD 290 – 306. Poisoned in AD 306 by Sima Yue, one of the warring princes.

Emperor Huai (AD 284 – 313) 晋怀帝
Sima Chi (司马炽), younger brother of Emperor Hui. During the War of Eight Princes, minority races from the north were invited by various factions to help in the infighting. They grew in strength and threatened the Western Jin dynasty. In AD 311, Emperor Huai was abducted by the Xiongnus and killed two years later.

Emperor Min 晋愍帝 (AD 270 – 317)
Sima Ye (司马邺), a nephew of Emperor Huai, came to the throne in AD 313 when his empire was very much in shambles. His abduction and death in AD 316 marked the end the Western Jin dynasty.

Emperor Yuan 晋元帝 (AD 276 – 323)
Sima Rui (司马睿), a great-grandson of Sima Yi (司马懿) who laid the foundation of the Eastern Jin dynasty by staging a coup in AD 249 and wresting power from the Cao family of the Wei Kingdom. Emperor Yuan founded the Eastern Jin dynasty south of the Yangtze River in AD

317 with the support of Wang Dao and other leading families of the region. He died in AD 322 during the rebellion by Wang Dun.

Emperor Ming 晋明帝 (AD 299 – 325)
Sima Shao (司马绍), eldest son of Emperor Yuan. Ruled from AD 322 to 325.

Emperor Cheng 晋成帝 (AD 321 – 342)
Sima Yan (司马衍), eldest son of Emperor Ming, ascended the throne in AD 325 at the age of five. His mother served as regent and his uncle, Yu Liang, headed the dominant faction at court until Liang's death in AD 340. He died in AD 342.

Emperor Kang 晋康帝 (AD 321 – 344)
Sima Yue (司马岳), younger brother of Emperor Cheng, reigned from AD 342 to 344.

Emperor Mu 晋穆帝
Sima Dan (司马聃), reigned from AD 344 to 361.

Emperor Ai (Lamented) 晋哀帝 (AD 340 – 365)
Sima Pi (司马丕), eldest son of Emperor Cheng, reigned from AD 362 – 365. Since he died after a short reign, he is known as Lamented Emperor.

Emperor Fei 晋废帝 (Deposed) (AD 342 – 386)
Sima Yi (司马奕), son of Emperor Cheng, reigned from AD 365. He was deposed in AD 371 by the ambitious warlord, Huan Wen.

Emperor Jian Wen 简文帝 (AD 320 – 372)
Sima Yu (司马昱), youngest son of Emperor Yuan, came to the throne in AD 371 as the puppet of Huan Wen but died the following year. He was a devoted patron of "pure conversation" and Buddhism.

Emperor Xiao Wu 孝武帝 (AD 362 – 396)
Sima Yao (司马曜), third son of Emperor Jian Wen, reigned from AD 372 to 396. A gifted and intelligent ruler but given to debauchery in later years of his reign. He died a victim of palace intrigue.

Emperor An 晋安帝 (AD 382 – 418)
Sima Dezong (司马德宗), the mentally-subnormal eldest son of Emperor Xiao Wu, reigned from AD 396 until he was poisoned in AD 418 by Liu Yu, the new military strongman who replaced Huan Xuan.

Emperor Gong 晋恭帝
Sima Dewen (司马德文), younger brother of Emperor An, was installed as a puppet of Liu Yu in AD 418. Liu deposed Emperor Gong in AD 420 and proclaimed himself emperor of the new Song dynasty.

Fu Jian 符坚 (AD 338 – 385)

Ruler of Former Qin who united northern China in AD 370. In AD 383 he led an army of 800,000 men to conquer the Eastern Jin dynasty in the south but was defeated by the vastly out-numbered Jin forces at the Fei River.

Fan Xuan 范宣 (AD 376 – 396)

A recluse scholar who established a reputation for purity and incorruptibility in his native Yuzhang county.

Gongsun Long 公孙龙

A famous dialectician during the Warring States Era (475 – 221 BC). He argued that a white horse is not a horse.

Gu Kaizhi 顾恺之 (AD 345 – 406)

A famous painter, calligrapher, poet and baffoon of the Eastern Jin dynasty.

Gu Shao 顾劭

A worthy man of the Wu Kingdom (AD 223 - 280) and son-in-law of the elder brother of its founder.

Gu Yan Xian 顾彦先 (AD 270 – 322)

An official of both the Western and Eastern Jin dynasties and a member of the distinguished Gu family in the Wu county.

Guan Ning 管宁 (AD 158 – 241)

A recluse scholar during the Eastern Han dynasty. He esteemed living in seclusion and never accepted any official post.

Guo Pu 郭璞 (AD 276 – 324)

An Eastern Jin literatus who was also deeply interested in the occult. Serving under Wang Dun, he was asked to make a prognostication when Wang planned a rebellion. His prognostication of failure caused him his life in AD 324.

Guo Xiang 郭象 (Died AD 312)

A Western Jin dynasty philosopher and brilliant conversationalist. He loved to study the philosophies of Lao Zi and Zhuang Zi. His commentary on "Zhuang Zi", an expanded version based on Xiang Xiu's, is still regarded as authoritative today.

Han Kangbo 韩康伯

A Western Jin dynasty official, an author and a nephew of Yin Hao.

Hao Long 郝隆

A humorous man who served as an official of Huan Wen around the middle of the fourth century.

He Yan 何晏 (AD 190 – 249)

An exceptionally gifted man whose mother became a concubine of Cao Cao when he was six years old. He was one of the founders of the Wei-Jin style of "pure conversation".

Hua Xin 华歆 (AD 157 – 231)

An official of the Eastern Han and Wei dynasties. Compared with Guan Ning, his mate during younger days who shunned public offices, Hua was much more interested in the pursuit of high office and fortunes.

Huan Wen 桓温 (AD 312 – 373)

Son of Huan Yi and a prominent member of the military family of Huan which rose in power during the Eastern Jin dynasty. As grand marshal, he was a virtual dictator and only his death in AD 373 prevented him from usurping the throne.

Huan Xuan 桓玄 (AD 369 – 404)

Youngest son of Huan Wen. In AD 404, he succeeded in usurping the throne of Eastern Jin dynasty. Three months later, he was overthrown and killed by another warlord, Liu Yu, who established the Song dynasty (AD 420 - 479) sixteen years later.

Huan Yi 桓彝 (AD 275 – 328)

Father of Huan Wen and one of the "Eight Free Spirits". He rose from poverty and obscurity to the rank of governor. He was killed in AD 328 while resisting a rebellion.

Huan Yi 桓伊 (Died AD 392)

A distant relative of Huan Wen and a brilliant general. A modest man of cultivated taste, he was acclaimed as the greatest flautist of his day and an accomplished zither player.

Huan Xiu 桓修 (Died AD 404)

A cousin of Huan Xuan. He served as governor of two provinces during Huan Xuan's brief usurpation in AD 404 but was killed by Liu Yu in the same year.

Ji Kang 嵇康 (AD 223 – 262)

A sensitive poet and musician of the Wei Kingdom and one of the leading figures among the Seven Worthies of the Bamboo Grove. He was executed as a "perverter of public morals " as a result of offending the powerful Sima family.

Jiang Quan 江权 (Died AD 375)

An Eastern Jin dynasty official noted for his punctilious behaviour.

Kang Fachang 康法畅

A monk probably of Sogdian origin who emigrated to China around the third decade of the fourth century. Reputedly an expert in judging character of people.

Kang Sengyuan 康僧渊 (AD 300 – 350)

A dharma master who was active in the Eastern Jin capital of Jiankang (present-day Nanjing). Born in China, probably of Sogdian parents, and possessed deep-set eyes and prominent nose.

Kong Rong 孔融 (AD 153 – 208)

A literatus of the Eastern Han dynasty during which he held many high posts. A descendant of Confucius. Proud and abrasive with his critical writings, he offended Cao Cao who subsequently found an excuse to execute him together with his family.

Liu Bei 刘备 (AD 162 – 233)

Founder of the Shu Han Kingdom (AD 221 – 263) and an arch enemy of Cao Cao. Died of an illness after a battle defeat.

Liu Chang 刘昶

A Western Jin official who was a great drinker.

Liu Kun 刘琨 (AD 271 – 318)

A Western Jin general. Fought long resistance battles against northern invaders.

Liu Ling 刘伶

A Western Jin literatus; one of the Seven Worthies of the Bamboo Grove. He showed contempt for contemporary ritual conventions but extolled the doctrines of Lao Zi and Zhuang Zi. Little is known about him apart from legends about his drinking habits.

Liu Dan 刘惔 (AD 311 – 347)

An Eastern Jin official. Brother-in-law of Xie An. A skilled conversationalist, he was a frequent guest at gatherings in the villa of Sima Yu (Emperor Jian Wen).

Lu Ji 陆机 (AD 261 – 303)

A Western Jin official and noted poet from a gentry family of the Wu Kingdom. He served under several princes of the Sima family and was executed during the War of the Eight Princes after being falsely accused of treachery.

Lu Ji 陆绩 (AD 187 – 219)

An official of the Wu Kingdom; an astronomer and commentator on the Book of Changes. He predicted his own death which occurred on his thirty-second year.

Lu Tui 陆退
An Eastern Jin official who lived in the second half of the fourth century. Son-in-law of Zhang Ping.

Lu Yun 陆云 (AD 262 – 303)
A Western Jin official. A noted poet but less famous as his elder brother, Lu Ji. Like his brother, too, he fell victim to intrigue in AD 303.

Lu Zhongdi 吕中悌 (Died AD 262)
A bosom friend of Ji Kang who shared his aversion to the rise of the Sima family in the Wei Kingdom. Both were executed for "perverting public morals" in AD 262.

Kuaiji, Prince of 会稽王(AD 364 – 402)
Sima Daozi (司马道之), fifth son of Emperor Jian Wen. His faction dominated the court of Eastern Jin from AD 385 to 402. A man given to corruption and debauchery, he was killed during Huan Xuan's rebellion in AD 402.

Ma Rong 马融 (AD 76 – 166)
An accomplished scholar and commentator of the Han dynasty. Despite his arrogance due to his being a relative of Empress Ma, there is doubt whether a man of his stature would have been jealous of Zheng Xuan and acted out of deadly spitefulness against his disciple.

Pang Tong 庞统 (AD 177 – 214)
An able man who served Liu Bei when he was a warlord in the final years of the Eastern Han dynasty.

Pei Qian 裴潜 (Died AD 244)
A Wei Kingdom official who rose to the rank of grand marshal.

Ruan Ji 阮籍 (AD 210 – 263)
A gifted poet and musician during the transitional period between the Wei and Jin dynasty. One of the Seven Worthies of the Bamboo Grove, he avoided political intrigues by maintaining a facade of continual drunkenness.

Ruan Xian 阮咸 (AD 234 – 305)
A nephew of Ruan Ji and a member of the Seven Worthies of the Bamboo Grove. A master musician who was extremely unconventional by nature, always poor and a great wine lover.

Ruan Xiu 阮修 (AD 270 – 312)
A nephew of Ruan Ji; made his name as an iconoclast who argued for the non-existence of ghosts.

Ruan Yu 阮裕 (AD 300 – 360)
A cousin of Ruan Ji, he served briefly at the court of Eastern Jin and, later,

as prefect in two prefectures. Thereafter, he declined further summons for office and lived retirement in the Shan prefecture.

Shan Tao 山涛 (AD 205 – 283)
A member of the Seven Worthies of the Bamboo Grove. Related to the Sima family on his mother's side, he finally shifted to their camp after they gained power in the AD 249 coup. At his death in AD 283, he was director of instruction, one of the highest Western Jin court offices.

Shi Chong 石崇 (AD 249 – 300)
A Western Jin official who was extremely rich. Noted for his rivalry of extravagance with Wang Kai. Killed in AD 300 during the War of the Eight Princes.

Sima Xiangru 司马相如 (179 – 117 BC)
A Western Han dynasty official and literatus noted for his pompous depiction of splendour of palatial life in poetic essays.

Srimitra, Reverend 高坐道人 (AD 310 – 340)
A monk from Central Asia who settled in Jiankang and enjoyed the respect and friendship of key members of the Estern Jin court.

Sun Chuo 孙绰 (AD 330 – 365)
Regarded as the top scholar of his day and much in demand as composer of obituaries and eulogies. He attempted to harmonise Buddhism and the contemplative life with Confucianism and an active political career.

Sun Shuao 孙叔敖
A premier of the Chu state around 600 BC.

Sun Zijing 孙子荆 (Died AD 282)
An Eastern Jin official and grandfather of Sun Chuo.

Wang Cheng 王承 (AD 275 – 320)
An official who served in both Jin dynasties and noted for his liberal administration. A man of calm disposition and few words.

Wang Can 王粲 (AD 177 – 217)
A noted poet and official of the Eastern Han dynasty. Died in AD 217 while accompanying Cao Cao on his campaign against Wu.

Wang Caizhi 王忱
Sixth son of Wang Xizhi and an Eastern Jin official who lived around late fourth century.

Wang Chen 王澄 (Died AD 392)
An Eastern Jin official and son of Wang Tanzhi. Given to unrestrained behaviour, he once rode to visit his sick father-in-law drunk and unclothed. Sometimes he also remained drunk for months at a time.

Wang Cheng (AD 269 – 312)

A Western Jin official who loved drinking and noted for his laxity of administration. Killed by Wang Dun whom he insulted on a visit.

Wang Dao 王导 (AD 276 – 339)

Principal supporter and adviser of Emperor Yuan who founded the Eastern Jin dynasty south of the Yangtze River in AD 317. He served as chancellor and in other important positions. A cousin of Wang Dun.

Wang Dun 王敦 (AD 266 – 324)

A powerful general both in Western and Eastern Jin dynasties; married to a daughter of emperor Wu and a cousin of Wang Dao. He staged two rebellions in AD 322 and 324 against a rising court faction. After failing in the second, he died of an illness in utter disgrace.

Wang Gong 王恭 (Died AD 388)

An Eastern Jin general and brother-in-law of Emperor Xiao Wu. Died in factional fighting in AD 397.

Wang Huizhi 王徽之 (Died AD 388)

Fifth son of Wang Xizhi, noted for his eccentric and undisciplined character. Never took seriously the few minor posts he occupied.

Wang Ji 王济 (AD 240 – 285)

A Western Jin general and brother-in-law of Emperor Wu.

Wang Kai 王恺

A Western Jin general and brother-in-law of one of the Sima princes. He and Shi Chong shared the reputation of being the most ostentatiously extravagent personalities of the Wei-Jin era.

Wang Lang 王朗 (Died AD 228)

A scholar and official of the Wei Kingdom.

Wang Meng 王濛 (AD 309 – 347)

An Eastern Jin official in the service of Wang Dao. A man of affable manner and quick wit who lived a simple life.

Wang Rong 王戎 (AD 234 – 305)

A Western Jin official noted for his extreme parsimony despite his enormous wealth. The youngest member of the Seven Worthies of the Bamboo Grove.

Wang Shu 王述 (AD 303 – 368)

An Eastern Jin official who rose to great ranks from an impoverished youth. Son of Wang Cheng and father of Wang Tanzhi.

Wang Tanzhi 王坦之 (AD 330 – 375)

A scholar and an official of Eastern Jin. A conservative ideologist, he bitterly opposed the libertinism of certain Taoist elements.

Wang Xizhi 王羲之 (AD 309 – 365)

One of China's greatest calligraphers. Nephew of Wang Dao. Held many high positions at the Eastern Jin court.

Wang Xianzhi 王献之 (AD 344 – 388)

Seventh son of Wang Xizhi. A calligrapher in his own right though never a match for his father. Married a princess of the Sima family in his second marriage. Rather undisciplined by nature.

Wang Xiu 王修 (AD 335 --358)

A skilled conversationalist and calligrapher at his death at the age of 23. A child prodigy who wrote a treatise critical of Liu Dan at the age of 11.

Wang Yun 王蕴 (AD 330 – 384)

An Eastern Jin official noted for his fairness in the appointment of officials and being unselfish and generous to a fault during a famine.

Wang Zhan 王湛 (AD 249 – 295)

A Western Jin official. Huge in size with a prominent forehead and nose, he gave people the false impression of being mentally subnormal.

Xi Jian 郗鉴 (AD 266 – 339)

A high official of Eastern Jin dynasty and father-in-law of Wang Xizhi.

Xiang Xiu 向秀 (AD 221 – 300)

A prominent member of the Seven Worthies of the Bamboo Grove and author of a lost commentary on Zhuang Zi, a book which strongly influenced the revival of philosophical Taoism during the third century. He entered government service in later life and rose to high positions in Western Jin.

Xie An 谢安 (AD 320 – 385)

A leading Eastern Jin dynasty politician and a prominent member of the powerful Xie family of the time. He entered government service after the age of forty and rose to the rank of chancellor. The greatest credit of his career was thwarting the invasion of Fu Jian from the north.

Xie Wanshi 谢万石 (AD 321 – 361)

A younger brother of Xie An. He failed as a military governor because of his arrogance and neglect. After being stripped off all offices and titles in AD 359, he avidly espoused the cause of the recluse until his death.

Xu Ning 许宁

An official of Western Jin during the early fourth century. At the recommendation of Huan Yi, Yu Liang gave him a post as a clerk of the Board of Civil Service. He went on to become a provincial governor.

Xu Xun 许珣

A recluse-poet who lived around the middle of the fourth century. Highly rated by contemporaries, he was credited as one of the earliest poets who employed Buddhist imagery and terminology in his poems. He steadfastly refused public office and died young.

Xu Zi 许子 (AD 97 --168)

A worthy man of the Eastern Han dynasty. Though poor throughout his life, he never accepted the many calls from high officials to enter government service.

Xun Can 荀粲 (AD 212 – 240)

An intellectual of the Wei Kingdom who shunned public office. He was so devoted to his wife, a member of the ruling house, that he died of grief after her premature death.

Xun Jubo 荀巨伯

A man who lived during the final years of the Eastern Han dynasty. Little is known about him.

Yang Xiu 杨修 (AD 178 – 220)

A gifted and quick-witted scholar who served under Cao Cao when the latter was chancellor of the Eastern Han dynasty. Too smart for Cao's liking, he was executed with the excuse of disorderly conduct. None of his voluminous writings survives.

Yin Hao 殷浩 (AD 306 – 356)

A famous conversationalist in his day, he rose to become generalissimo of the central army of Eastern Jin. After a sound defeat in a move to recover the north in AD 353, he was dismissed and exiled. He spent his final years studying Buddhist scriptures.

Yin Hongqiao 殷洪乔

An official of Western Jin during the early fourth century; father of Yin Hao.

Yin Zhongkan 殷仲堪 (Died AD 400)

A governor during Eastern Jin. He was forced to commit suicide by Huan Xuan in AD 400 in a factional struggle.

Yu Liang 庾亮 (AD 289 – 340)

An influential and well-respected politician of Eastern Jin. From AD 326 to 340, he was the dominant power behind the throne of his nephew, Emperor Cheng, who ascended the throne at the age of five.

Yuan Xiaoni 袁孝尼
A scholar who was a contemporary of Ji Kang. He was said to be extremely diffident but obsessed with with literary pursuits.

Yuan Yue 袁悦 (Died AD 389)
An official of Eastern Jin who made a close study of the classic, "Intrigues of the Warring States", and attempted to apply its wily principles by advising one of the Sima princes to seize power. His conspiracy backfired and he was executed in AD 389.

Zhang Han 张翰
A Western Jin official and poet who was active during the first quarter of the fourth century.

Zhang Ping 张凭
An Eastern Jin official who was active around the middle of the fourth century. He was a talented writer who produced a commentary on the Analects much admired in his day.

Zhang Xuanzhi 张玄之
A member of a prominent gentry family and a high official of Eastern Jin who was active in the second half of the fourth century.

Zheng Xuan 郑玄 (AD 122 – 200)
One of the greatest commentators on the classics of all time and a disciple of Ma Rong. Died of illness during the civil war in the final years of the Han dynasty.

Zhi Daolin 支道林 (AD 316 – 366)
The best known and most influential monk of Eastern Jin. Born of a northen gentry family, he was not ordained until the age of 25. A popular lecturer in Buddhism and an active participant in "pure conversation", he counted among his lay disciples many of the day's great figues like Xie An, Yin Hao and Wang Xizhi.

Zhou Chu 周处 (AD 240 – 299)
A Western Jin general who in his youth was a bully and regarded by his countrymen as a scourge. He reformed his ways, served the government and made a reputation for being a good administrator. He was killed in battle while resisting a rebellion.

Zhou Yi 周顗 (AD 269 – 322)
A high official of both Western and Eastern Jin. His career was marred by his bibulous habits and he eventually died a bloody death after insulting the rebel Wang Dun in AD 322.

Zu Yue 祖约 (Died AD 330)
A governor and nobleman of Eastern Jin. In AD 328, after failing in a

rebellion against the Jin court, he fled north to seek refuge with the Xiongnu ruler Shi Le, who eventually put him to death with 100 members of his clan.

Zhu Fashen 竺法深 (AD 286 – 374)

A Buddhist monk who enjoyed the favour of emperors and courtiers at the Eastern Jin capital of Jiankang. He is said to be a younger brother of Wang Dun.

Zhuge Dan 诸葛诞 (Died AD 258)

An official of the Wei Kingdom and a cousin of Zhuge Liang. In AD 257, he rebelled against the Sima faction in Wei but was defeated and executed the following year.

Zhuge Liang 诸葛亮 (AD 181 – 234)

The legendary strategist of Liu Bei. When Liu founded the Shu Kingdom in AD 221, Zhuge became his chief adviser and commander of all military operations. He died in campaign against the Wu Kingdom.

Zhuge Jin 诸葛瑾 (AD 174 – 241)

Elder brother of Zhuge Liang. He served Sun Quan, founder of the Wu Kingdom. Despite the fact that his brother Zhuge Liang was serving the rival state of Shu, he was able to maintain an impeccable loyalty to Wu.

《亚太漫画系列》

魏晋万花筒

世说新语

作者：刘义庆
编著：蔡志忠
翻译：张家荣

亚太图书（新）有限公司出版